ELAINE O'REILLY

Level 2

Series Editors: Andy Hopkins and Jocelyn Potter

Pearson Education Limited
Edinburgh Gate, Harlow,
Essex CM20 2JE, England
and Associated Companies throughout the world.

ISBN-13: 978-0-582-42764-8
ISBN-10: 0-582-42764-9

This edition first published 2000

5 7 9 10 8 6

NEW EDITION

Copyright © Penguin Books Ltd 2000
Illustrations by Andrew Stewart
Cover design by Bender Richardson White

Typeset by Bender Richardson White
Set in 11/14pt Bembo
Printed and bound in China
GCC/05

Published by Pearson Education Limited in association with
Penguin Books Ltd, both companies being subsidiaries of Pearson Plc

For a complete list of titles available in the Penguin Readers series, please write to your local
Pearson Education office or to: Penguin Readers Marketing Department,
Pearson Education, Edinburgh Gate, Harlow, Essex CM20 2JE.

Contents

Introduction

Every student on the bus turned to the nearest person and repeated:
'Have a lovely day!' They always did this. It was School Procedure.

Eden City is in another world. It is very different from our world. The people in Eden City are happy. Always happy. They never fight. They are never ill. They are never old. They are all young and beautiful. Everybody works and studies in Eden City. They do the same things every day. Nothing changes. They love their quiet, happy world . . .

But then student BZXY741 meets Eve, and she tells him about another world – the Real World. He doesn't understand. She takes him on a journey to the Real World and he sees a lot of strange things.

But who is Eve? Why is she different? What does she want from BZ? And is her world really better than Eden City?

Elaine O'Reilly was born in South Africa. She now has a bookshop in Rome, and she writes for children's television. She has two dogs, three cats and a daughter.

Chapter 1   'Happy is Good'

The School for Higher Studies in Happiness was about five kilometres outside Eden City. Every day, a bus took the students from the centre of town to the school. On the way, the students sang. There were a lot of students on the bus and the noise was wonderful.

'I'm H-A-P-P-Y,
I'm H-A-P-P-Y,
Every day, in every way,
I'm H-A-P-P-Y.'

Student BZXY741 sat behind the driver. His singing was louder than the other students'. He sang well and he loved to sing.

'Happy is good
And sad is bad,
I'm H-A-P-P-Y.'

He really was very happy. He was the best student of the year, the winner for the Best Smile. Every student and every teacher at the school loved him. He looked out of the window at the white streets of Eden City, at the red and blue buildings, at the flowers and trees. The city was beautiful in the sunlight – not real sunlight, of course. There were no people on the streets. It was Work Time.

'I'm happy when I work.
I'm happy when I play.

Tomorrow I'm going to be happier,
Happier than today.'

In Eden City, some people worked and some people studied. But workers weren't different from students. Everybody was happy.

The bus drove through the streets and into the gardens of the school. Flowers of every colour turned their heads and watched. The birds in the trees sang: *'Have a lovely day!'* Every student on the bus turned to the nearest person and repeated: *'Have a lovely, lovely day!'* They always did this. It was School Procedure.

BZXY741 turned to the girl on his left. She smiled at him. It was a wonderful smile, warm and friendly.

'She's very pretty,' he thought. 'But she's different. How is she

different? Of course! Her eyes . . . it's the colour of her eyes!'

They were grey eyes, not blue. But everybody in the school had blue eyes. Why did she have grey eyes? Grey wasn't a good colour. He remembered Lesson 836: *'Bad Colours. Grey is one of the worst colours. It is a sad colour. The colour of cold days. The colour of dark skies. It is an old colour.'* But this girl's eyes were beautiful. He looked at her again. She smiled again.

'Have a lovely day,' said BZXY741.

She didn't answer him. There was a question in her strange grey eyes. And BZXY741 didn't understand, because in his world there were no questions. In the world of Eden City, there were only answers.

Chapter 2 'Be a Good Friend'

The bus stopped outside the front of the school and the students got off. BZXY741 looked for the girl. He wanted to say, 'Enjoy your lessons', but he couldn't see her. He followed the other students into the building and walked slowly to his classroom. He thought about the girl with grey eyes.

'What was that look in her eyes? Who is she? Perhaps she's new here.'

Some of his friends turned round and called to him, 'BZ! You're going to be late.'

'I'm coming,' he answered, 'I'm coming.'

The first three hours of lessons that morning were Life Studies: *'Be a Good Friend.'* Then there were two hours of *'Do People Like You?'* BZ really enjoyed these lessons, so he stopped thinking about the girl on the bus.

At midday, the students had lunch in the Flower Garden. BZ sat down at a table under a big tree with beautiful flowers. It was a warm day and the smell of the flowers was strong. The birds sang the menu: 'Hamburger or sandwich, chicken with salad, chocolate ice cream. Enjoy your lunch!'

BZ took a drink from his glass of cold green juice. Wonderful. He closed his eyes and thought for a minute about his future. It was a good future.

'I'm going to be on The Team,' he thought. 'I *know* that I'm going to be on The Team.' The Team worked for The People's Happiness. People were happy because they made the laws. The Team's work was important. They were the most important people in Eden City. That was BZXY741's future and he felt very happy about it . . .

When he opened his eyes, he saw the girl with grey eyes at his table.

'Hi, BZ!' she said.

'Hello.' He smiled, and then he remembered his first lesson of the morning: *'Be a good friend. Give something nice to somebody.'* So he pushed his plate across the table to her.

'Please have some of my salad. It's very good.'

She laughed. 'No, thanks. I don't like the school food.'

BZ didn't understand. He started to feel strange. Didn't she know School Procedure: *'Always say yes'*? 'No' wasn't friendly. The girl laughed again.

'BZ! Don't look so worried. I like the word. I often say it. No, no, no, no! The sky doesn't fall on my head!'

'I don't understand.'

'It's OK. Forget it.' She moved her chair near his chair. 'Listen, BZ,' she said quietly, 'I know everything about you. I think you're a wonderful person. I want to help you. And I think that you can help me. And a lot of other people, too.'

BZ looked at her carefully for a minute. 'I think I understand now,' he said slowly. 'This is a *Friendly Joke*. Of course – yes! It's very strange, but very funny!' And he laughed very loudly. She put her hand on his arm.

4

'It's not a joke. I want to tell you something. Something very important. It will change your life. And perhaps the lives of everybody here in Eden City.'

Then the birds sang, '*Go back to work, boys and girls. Back to work.*'

The students in the Flower Garden stood up. BZ stood up, too.

'I'm sorry. I don't understand this conversation. It's very interesting, but I don't understand it.' He smiled his best smile. The girl didn't smile back at him.

'Listen,' she said, 'there's a dance tonight at the House of Music. I'll see you there. Please come. It's very, very important. For you and me. Please say that you'll come.'

'All right,' said BZ. 'I'll come.' He thought, 'Do I want to meet this strange girl again? I don't know. I don't understand her.' But he had to go. He couldn't say no. It wasn't friendly. It wasn't School Procedure.

Chapter 3   'Dancing is Good for You'

When BZ arrived at the House of Music, the girl was there at the door.

'Hello,' he said. 'Isn't it a beautiful evening? You look very nice.' Lesson 672: *'Starting a Conversation.'* The girl said nothing. She took his hand and they went into the building.

The dance started. People moved slowly with the music. It was a new song, 'Dancing is Good For You'. Blue and white lights shone on the faces of the dancers. BZ and the girl began to dance.

'Dancing is good for you,' sang BZ quietly. *'Do it every day.'*

'Do you know my number, BZ?' the girl asked.

'I'm sorry, I don't.'

Each student had a number. The number was on the inside of their left arms. The girl showed him her white arm . . . there was no number there!

'But where is it?' asked BZ. 'You have to have a number!'

'I don't. I have a name.' She smiled. 'My name is Eve.'

For a minute, BZ felt afraid. *'Be the Same – Different is Ugly.'*

But this girl, with her grey eyes and her warm smile, wasn't ugly. She was beautiful.

'What's happening to me?' he thought.

Then two of his friends danced past them.

'Hello, BZ! Are you having a good time? What's wrong with you? You don't look happy.'

'Oh, but I am happy!' said BZ quickly. 'I'm having a wonderful time. Isn't the music wonderful?'

'It's great! See you later, BZ.'

'BZ,' said Eve, 'I have to talk to you . . .' The music changed. This time it was fast and loud. The lights changed to red and yellow.

'Let's dance!' said BZ. 'I love this song.'

'No. I'm tired. I don't want to dance.'

'Then let's have a glass of juice.'

'No. I want to leave here and talk to you.'

'But the dance . . . ?'

'There will be a thousand other dances. Let's go.'

He followed her out into the quiet street. They walked but didn't speak. Then they sat down near some water. The water smelled lovely and the sound of it was music.

'What do you want to tell me?' BZ asked.

'How much do you really understand about Eden City? What do you really know about our lives?'

'Life is for Happiness. Love Your Friends . . .'

'No, no, no, BZ! Those are only words. They teach you them at school. But, they don't mean anything.'

'Don't mean anything? How can you say that?'

'Do you know about the real world, BZ? Do you *want* to know about the real world?'

'What real world? I don't understand . . .'

'This isn't the real world. Eden City isn't real. Nothing in Eden City is real. The air, the sky . . . look up, BZ! It's not real!'

'Then where *is* the real world?'

'It's above us. Nearly 500 kilometres above us, there's another world. The real world. There, people live real lives. Nobody tells them, 'Think this. Feel that.' They live in families, not only with friends. They love, they hate, they fight. They get ill, they get old, they die. They're free!'

BZ put his hands over his eyes.

'Oh, no. That's a sad life.'

'No, it isn't. It's the best life. We aren't really living. We aren't free. We have no freedom. We can't change anything. The Team makes the laws for us. We have to listen to them. We have to think their ideas, feel their feelings. That's not freedom, BZ, believe me.'

'I *don't* believe you.' BZ stood up. 'And I don't want to listen to you. I want to forget all this. I don't like it.'

But he couldn't forget. He knew that. Eve's words were in his head, and now he had questions about his life. He felt unhappy for the first time. He walked away from her.

'Wait, BZ! I'm sorry. I know you're unhappy. But you have to believe me. I can show you. I can take you up into the real world. Now. Tonight!'

Chapter 4   A Journey to the Real World

BZ felt very strange. He followed Eve through the streets of Eden City. He was afraid. His head hurt.

'Why am I doing this? Where's Eve taking me? What's going to happen?'

They were in Eden City, but there were no trees, no flowers here. Everything was very different. The streets were small and dark.

'Where are we, Eve? Do you know this place?'

'Ssshhh! We're nearly there.'

They stopped. They were nearly at the end of the street. Eve put a finger to her mouth.

'Look into the next street,' she said very quietly.

BZ moved closer to the building and looked round it. At the end of the street there was a wall. In the wall there was a large door. There were two men with guns at the door.

'What is it, Eve? What's behind that door?'

'That's the lift. They bring things down from the real world in it. It leaves three times each day. The next journey is in five minutes. We have to get inside the lift.'

'But how? How do we get past those men?'

'Look again . . . Do you see those big boxes? They bring things down from the real world in them. There's nothing inside them now. We can go in one of them. Quick! Follow me!'

She moved as quietly as a cat. And, very quickly, she jumped inside one of the boxes. BZ followed her.

They waited. A minute later, he heard the lift doors – they opened. One of the men shouted, 'Let's put these boxes into the lift.' Their box started to move, and BZ felt afraid.

'This box feels really heavy!' said one of the men.

'You're tired. Push it again!'

And suddenly they were in the lift. The doors closed and they started on their journey.

'There!' said Eve. 'That wasn't difficult, BZ.'

He could feel her cold arm next to

his arm. He couldn't see anything. He was worried. For the first time in his life, he was cold and hungry. He didn't want to think about his warm room, at the Friends' Happy Home. He wanted to be there. He didn't want to think about dinner with the other students. His friends. 'Will I see them again?' he thought.

He thought about his past life. His life before Eve. Every day was a long, sunny day. Evenings with friends at the Sports Centre, the Games Park or the House of Music. 'Why does Eve think that life in Eden City is bad? Freedom? What did she mean?' Then he thought about his future. 'Will this journey change my future?' He didn't understand.

'Eve?'

'Yes?'

'Why *me*? Why do you want to show *me* the real world?'

She found his hand in the dark. The lift moved very fast.

'Because I think you're a good person. You're an intelligent person. And I know that you're going to be on The Team. You'll make laws for Eden City. You can change things. You can give people their freedom. You can help them and they'll live really happily.'

BZ thought about these things. The idea of change was very strange to him. A new idea.

'And you, Eve? Why are you different from the people in our world? You don't have a number. Your eyes are a different colour. You want to change things. Who are you really?'

'I can't answer these questions now. But wait. You'll learn the answers in the end.' She put her cold fingers on his face. 'Don't be afraid, BZ. Believe me, it's going to be all right.'

The lift moved more slowly now. Suddenly, it stopped.

Eve and BZ climbed out of the box.

'We're here,' Eve said. 'This is the real world.'

Chapter 5   The Real World

The lift doors opened and Eve and BZ went out into the real world. It was very early morning. The light, the air, the smells were very different. Then BZ heard the noise. He put his hands over his ears.

'What is it, Eve? What's that strange noise?'

'It's the traffic . . . the cars and buses and taxis. Nearly everybody here has a car. They drive everywhere. Now they're driving to work. Don't worry.'

'But where are we?'

'We're in London. It's a city. It was a beautiful city, but now there are a lot of people here. There's a lot of traffic.'

Eve took BZ's hand in her hand and they walked down the street. Tall buildings on their left and on their right shut out the light. People walked quickly past them. BZ looked at them. They were small and thin. Their faces were tired and worried.

'Are these people happy and free?' he asked Eve.

'They don't look happy, I know. But they're free. They don't *have to* be happy. The people in Eden City *have to* be happy,' Eve said.

She stopped. 'Look, here's a café. Let's have some breakfast.'

They went into the café and sat down at the table opposite the window. A waitress in a black dress came to their table. She was a short woman and she wasn't thin.

'Hello,' she said. 'What will you have?' She smiled. She didn't have all her teeth. BZ looked away.

'What would you like, BZ?' Eve asked.

'. . . I . . . I . . . don't know.'

'Would you like a hot breakfast?' the waitress said. 'Some eggs, perhaps?'

BZ couldn't look at her. 'Yes, that's fine.'

'I'll have that, too,' said Eve. 'And two cups of coffee.'

The waitress went to the kitchen. Eve watched BZ. He could feel her eyes on him.

'What's wrong, BZ?'

'That woman . . . the waitress. Why is she fat? Why is she ugly?'

Eve laughed. 'I don't think she's ugly. She's got a nice, kind face. She's got problems with her teeth, but perhaps she hasn't got the money for . . .'

'Money? What's that?'

'Oh, BZ, BZ! Money is one of the most important things in this world . . . in the real world. Here people get money for their work. They use money when they buy a house. They use money for clothes and food.' She showed him: 'Look, this is money. These are five-pound notes.'

BZ looked at the dirty paper in Eve's hand. It didn't look important.

'When you work,' he asked, 'they give you this . . . money? And then what?'

'It isn't easy . . . But here's our breakfast. I'll tell you more about money later.'

The waitress put the food on the table. It smelled strange.

'Eat it, BZ. It's good.'

It *was* good. BZ ate everything on his plate, because he was very hungry. He began to feel better.

'What are you going to show me now?' he asked Eve.

Suddenly, there was a noise at the window. BZ looked out. Through the window, he could see a man's face. A strange, ugly face. The eyes were closed and the mouth was open. The man put his finger to his mouth.

'Eve, who is that? Who's that man?'

'It's all right. He's only a beggar.'

'A beggar?'

'Beggars have no money. So they can't buy food. They have to ask other people for money.'

'But why doesn't he have a job?'

'Look at his eyes. He can't see.'

BZ felt ill. 'Please, Eve, take me away from this place. I don't like it.'

'All right. I'll take you out of London. We'll go into the country. I'll show you places with trees and birds and pretty gardens. The air is clean and the sky is blue . . . real sky.'

Eve paid for their breakfast and they went out into the street. The air was grey and dirty. BZ didn't feel well.

'Don't worry, BZ. We'll go now.' She put up her hand and

14

shouted, 'Taxi!' A big black car stopped and BZ and Eve got in.

'Hadley Wood, please,' she said to the driver.

Chapter 6   A Taxi Journey

The taxi drove slowly through the traffic. BZ looked out of the window at the people in their cars. He thought of his friends in Eden City. They never looked bored or unhappy. But these people . . . 'Eve thinks that this world . . . the real world . . . is wonderful,' he thought. 'But why?' He looked at her and she smiled at him.

'I know, I know. But wait. When we get out of the city, you'll see.'

Slowly they began to leave the city behind them. There weren't many cars now, and the taxi went faster. From his window, BZ could see flowers and trees. The real world started to look different. Different from the grey streets, the grey air, the grey faces. There were houses, big beautiful houses with lovely gardens.

'Who lives in those houses?' he asked.

'Those are rich people's houses.'

'Rich people? Who are they?'

The taxi driver heard their conversation. He started to laugh. 'Who *is* this? Is he from another world? "Who are rich people?" Hah! Is this a joke? Is he stupid or something?'

'No,' said Eve quietly, 'it's not a joke. And he's not stupid.'

'OK. Tell him about rich people.'

'I told you about money, BZ,' she said. 'Do you remember? Money's very important here. Some people have a lot of money. Those people are the rich people. And some people haven't got much money.'

'Taxi drivers . . . ,' said the driver.

15

'Can people get a lot of money easily?' asked BZ.

The taxi driver laughed angrily. 'Can a cat catch a lot of birds easily? Can people fly through the air easily?'

'Don't listen to him, BZ. It isn't easy, but people *can* make a lot of money. They usually have to work very hard, but then they can be rich.'

'That's a dream,' said the driver. 'Only a dream.'

Again, BZ thought about Eden City. Nobody was different there. They did different jobs, of course, but they had the same clothes, the same food. They lived in Happy Homes, and the homes were all the same.

'Eve,' he said, 'why do you think it's better here? Why do you like it?'

'I'm happier here. I love the noise, the people. I love the weather, because it changes often. People here can be different, and I like that. I like it because . . . it's my home.'

'What do you mean?'

16

'Eden City isn't my home. I wasn't born there.'

'I don't understand. Where were you born?'

'Here, in London. BZ, I've got a family.'

'A . . . what?' His face was red. He couldn't look at Eve. He was very embarrassed. The word 'family' was a bad word. One of the worst words. He felt ill.

'Don't be embarrassed,' Eve said. 'In the real world, everybody has a family.'

'Don't tell me! I don't want to hear!' He turned away from her and looked out of the window. They were in the country.

'Stop here, please,' Eve said to the taxi driver.

She paid the driver and they got out of the car. They walked down the road. They didn't speak.

BZ looked up at the sky. It was bigger, higher and bluer than the sky in Eden City. There was a little wind.

'Isn't it beautiful?' Eve asked. 'Don't you like the wind on your face and in your hair?'

'It's very interesting.'

'And listen to the birds. These are real birds.'

They turned down a small road. At the end of the road there was a big, old house. Eve took BZ's hand.

'Come,' she said. 'That's my house. I want you to meet my family.'

Chapter 7   Eve's Family

BZ and Eve stood in the front garden. There were a lot of trees in the garden, and a child's bicycle. 'I don't want to come in,' said BZ. But the front door of the house opened. Two small boys ran out.

'Eve! It's Eve! She's home!' they shouted happily. Eve opened her arms and they ran into them.

'BZ, these boys are my brothers. This is Daniel, he's nine. And this is Peter, he's six.'

'Hello,' said BZ. 'This is nice.' But he wasn't happy. He was very embarrassed. In Eden City, people didn't have brothers and sisters. They were born in the New Life Centre and then they moved to the Little People's Park. Later, they worked or they studied.

The younger boy took BZ's hand. 'Would you like to see Miranda? Her babies were born last week. They're lovely.'

Eve laughed when she saw BZ's face. 'Miranda's our dog, BZ. Don't worry.'

'And then,' said the other boy, 'I'll show you my new camera. Eve gave it to me for my birthday. It's wonderful.'

'Later, boys, later,' said Eve. 'Perhaps BZ would like to wash his hands. Where are Mum and Dad?'

'They went to the supermarket,' said Daniel.

'They'll be back in ten or fifteen minutes,' said Peter.

Eve smiled. 'Good. Can you take BZ inside and show him the bathroom?'

BZ followed the boys into the house. It was dark inside. There was a smell of fruit.

'It's a funny house,' he thought. 'Everything's old. The pictures on the walls are strange, too.' He looked at a photograph of a pretty girl in a long white dress. 'Is that Eve . . . ?'

'Here's the bathroom,' said Daniel.

'We'll wait for you in the garden,' said Peter.

BZ closed the bathroom door and turned on the water. He looked at his face.

'Do I look different? Am I changing?' He washed his hands and face. 'This is a . . . a . . . family, and it's not bad. Eve's little brothers aren't ugly. They're very nice . . .'

Suddenly he felt afraid. 'I'm not thinking the right things! Why am I here? Why aren't I in my classroom in Eden City? This is wrong. Wrong!'

He opened the bathroom door and went out. He could hear people in another room. A door opened.

'BZ,' Eve called. 'Come into the living-room.' He walked into a big, sunny room.

'Dad, I'd like you to meet BZ. He's a student at my school. BZ, this is my father.'

When BZ saw her father's face, he suddenly felt ill. The man was old. His hair was white and his face was ugly. BZ couldn't move. He couldn't take the old man's hand.

'It's all right,' said Eve's father. 'I understand. I'm sixty years old, and in your world you don't see old men.'

'Sixty!' thought BZ. 'How is this possible? In Eden City there *are* no people older than twenty-five.'

In BZ's world of young and beautiful people, life ended at twenty-five. On their twenty-fifth birthday, people went happily to the Long Dream. That was the Procedure.

The living-room door opened. 'Hello!' said a woman. 'We have a visitor, I see.'

'BZ, this is my mother.' BZ looked quickly at the woman, then he looked away again. She was old, too. But it was worse in her. She had Eve's beautiful face, but it was old and tired. One day, Eve, too . . .

BZ turned and ran out of the house, out of the garden. He had to get away. Away from these bad things.

'Wait, BZ! Please wait for me!' It was Eve. He stopped and waited for her. 'Please, please try the real world. I'll show you more . . .'

'I don't want to see more. Please take me back to Eden City. I hate this. I'm sorry.'

Eve looked at him angrily. Then she said, 'All right. I was wrong. You *aren't* different. You *can't* understand. You can't understand because you really are a student of Eden City. Wait here. I'll call a taxi and it will take us back into town.'

7 Answer the questions. Find the words in *italics* in your dictionary.

  a Are you *alive*?

  b Do you see *beggars* in the streets?

  c Do you *dream* in the daytime?

  d Do you feel *embarrassed* when you make stupid mistakes?

  e What is your *reaction* to a very cold bath?

  f Do you find *traffic* in people's houses?

After you read

  8 Who is Eve? Why did she take BZ to the real world?

  9 Talk to other students. Would you like to live in Eden City? Why (not)?

Writing

10 You are from Eden City. You are going to meet Eve, and you can ask her about life in the real world. Write ten questions for her.

11 BZ is now on The Team. Tomorrow is Eve's twenty-fifth birthday. Write a letter from BZ to Eve.

12 You visited Eden City for the first time yesterday. Write about it for a newspaper. What did you think of it?

13 You now work in the Office of The People's Happiness. What is important in life? What do you want people to believe? Write a new song.

Answers for the Activities in this book are available from your local office or alternatively write to: Penguin Readers Marketing Department, Pearson Education, Edinburgh Gate, Harlow, Essex CM20 2JE.